THE POWER OF REGENERATIVE AGRICULTURE

TRANSFORMING AGRICULTURE FOR ENVIRONMENTAL, ECONOMIC, AND SOCIAL SUSTAINABILITY

MICHAEL BARTON

Book
Bound Studios

To the farmers, environmentalists, policymakers, and all who strive for a more sustainable and equitable future through regenerative agriculture. Your dedication and hard work inspire me to do my part in advocating for and supporting this vital movement.

Sincerely, Michael Barton

"If we can't afford to take good care of the land that feeds us, we're in an insurmountable mess."

WENDELL BERRY

CONTENTS

Foreword   ix
Introduction   xi

1. THE PRINCIPLES OF REGENERATIVE
   AGRICULTURE   1
   Soil Health and Fertility   1
   Water Management   2
   Biodiversity   3
   Crop Rotation and Intercropping   4
   Livestock Management   5
   Chapter Summary   7

2. THE HISTORY OF REGENERATIVE
   AGRICULTURE   9
   Traditional Agricultural Practices   9
   The Rise of Industrial Agriculture   11
   The Emergence of Regenerative Agriculture   12
   Chapter Summary   14

3. THE ENVIRONMENTAL BENEFITS OF
   REGENERATIVE AGRICULTURE   17
   Soil Carbon Sequestration   17
   Water Conservation   18
   Pesticide and Fertilizer Reduction   21
   Biodiversity Conservation   22
   Chapter Summary   24

4. THE ECONOMIC BENEFITS OF REGENERATIVE
   AGRICULTURE   27
   Increased Efficiency and Productivity   27
   Reduced Input Costs   28
   Increased Profitability   29
   Community Development   30
   Chapter Summary   32

5. THE SOCIAL BENEFITS OF REGENERATIVE
   AGRICULTURE   35
   Improved Public Health   35
   Enhanced Rural Livelihoods   37
   Increased Food Security   38
   Strengthened Communities   39
   Chapter Summary   42

6. CHALLENGES AND BARRIERS TO
   IMPLEMENTING REGENERATIVE
   AGRICULTURE   45
   Lack of Knowledge and Resources   45
   Limited Market Demand   46
   Regulatory Barriers   47
   Cultural and Social Barriers   49
   Chapter Summary   51

7. SOLUTIONS AND STRATEGIES FOR
   OVERCOMING CHALLENGES   53
   Education and Training Programs   53
   Research and Development   55
   Policy and Regulatory Reform   56
   Market Development and Support   57
   Chapter Summary   60

8. THE FUTURE OF REGENERATIVE
   AGRICULTURE   63
   The Role of Regenerative Agriculture in
   Addressing Climate Change   63
   The Potential for Regenerative Agriculture to
   Feed the World   65
   The Role of Government and Policy in
   Supporting Regenerative Agriculture   66
   Chapter Summary   69

   Conclusion   71

   Afterword   73
   Acknowledgments   75
   About the Author   77
   From the Author   79

FOREWORD

As a long-time advocate for sustainable agriculture, I am thrilled to introduce *The Power of Regenerative Agriculture*. This comprehensive guide offers a unique perspective on the future of farming, exploring the principles, benefits, and strategies of regenerative agriculture.

Through this book, you will learn about regenerative agriculture's environmental, economic, and social impacts and the challenges and solutions for implementing this sustainable approach. You will also gain insight into the potential of regenerative agriculture to create a more sustainable and equitable future for all.

Regenerative agriculture is a critical part of the solution to many challenges we face as a global community. From climate change to food security to social justice, regenerative agriculture offers a holistic and sustainable approach to addressing these challenges. This book will inspire you to learn more about regenerative agriculture and how you can be a part of this important movement.

With its accessible and engaging style, *The Power of Regener-*

ative Agriculture is a valuable resource for farmers, environmentalists, policymakers, and anyone interested in the future of food and farming. I recommend it as a starting point for anyone looking to learn more about this transformative approach to agriculture.

Sincerely, Michael Barton

INTRODUCTION

Regenerative agriculture is a growing movement gaining traction worldwide as more and more people recognize the need for a shift toward more sustainable and equitable food systems. In this chapter, we will explore the definition of regenerative agriculture, the need for these practices, and their numerous benefits. By understanding the foundations of regenerative agriculture, we can gain insights into the potential for these practices to create a more sustainable and equitable food system for the future.

DEFINITION OF REGENERATIVE AGRICULTURE

Regenerative agriculture is a holistic approach to farming and land management that aims to restore and enhance the health and fertility of the soil, as well as the biodiversity of the ecosystem. This approach is based on sustainability, resilience, and regenerative capacity principles. Furthermore, it seeks to create a closed-loop system in which waste is minimized, and resources are used efficiently.

In other words, regenerative agriculture aims to create a farming system that is sustainable in the long term and able to regenerate and improve the natural resources it relies upon. This includes the soil, water, and biological diversity of the ecosystem in which it is practiced. By prioritizing these principles, regenerative agriculture seeks to create a more sustainable and resilient food system that benefits the environment and the people who depend on it.

Many different practices and techniques fall under the umbrella of regenerative agriculture, including cover cropping, composting, crop rotation, intercropping, agroforestry, and managed grazing, among others. In addition, these practices are often integrated and customized to suit the specific needs and conditions of a given farm or region.

One of the key goals of regenerative agriculture is to improve the health and fertility of the soil. Soil is a vital natural resource that provides the foundation for all plant growth and is essential for producing high-quality crops. Unfortunately, many modern farming practices have degraded the soil, leading to decreased crop yields and increased reliance on synthetic inputs such as fertilizers and pesticides. Regenerative agriculture seeks to reverse this trend by using practices that enhance the soil's structure, biology, and nutrient content, such as cover cropping, composting, and reducing tillage.

In addition to improving soil health, regenerative agriculture also seeks to conserve water and reduce erosion, enhance biodiversity, and integrate livestock in a way that benefits the ecosystem's overall health. These practices can help to create a more sustainable and resilient food system that can adapt and thrive in the face of challenges such as climate change and population growth.

Overall, regenerative agriculture offers a promising approach to farming and land management that has the potential to create a more sustainable and equitable food system for the future. By incorporating these principles and practices into our farming and land management systems, we can work towards a brighter future for agriculture and the environment.

THE NEED FOR REGENERATIVE AGRICULTURE

The need for regenerative agriculture is pressing and urgent, as it is driven by several complex and interconnected factors that threaten our food system's long-term sustainability and resilience.

One of the primary drivers of the need for regenerative agriculture is the negative impacts of industrial agriculture on the environment. Industrial agriculture is a model of farming that relies on monoculture, synthetic inputs such as pesticides and fertilizers, and large-scale mechanization. While this model has successfully increased food production in the short term, it has also had serious negative environmental consequences. These include soil erosion, water pollution, habitat destruction, and biodiversity loss.

Another factor contributing to the need for regenerative agriculture is the declining fertility of the soil. The soil is a vital natural resource that provides the foundation for all plant growth and is essential for producing high-quality crops. Unfortunately, many modern farming practices have degraded the soil, leading to decreased crop yields and increased reliance on synthetic inputs such as fertilizers and pesticides. This trend is unsustainable and threatens our food system's long-term productivity and viability.

Finally, the negative impacts of climate change on food

production are also driving the need for regenerative agriculture. Climate change is causing rising temperatures, extreme weather events, and changing rainfall patterns that seriously threaten food production. To ensure a secure and sustainable food supply in the face of these challenges, shifting towards more sustainable and regenerative practices is essential.

Overall, the need for regenerative agriculture is clear and pressing. By shifting towards more sustainable and regenerative practices, we can work towards a more secure and sustainable food system that can better withstand future challenges.

THE BENEFITS OF REGENERATIVE AGRICULTURE

The benefits of regenerative agriculture are extensive and far-reaching and go beyond increasing crop yields and improving food security. By focusing on the health and fertility of the soil and promoting biodiversity, regenerative agriculture can support the long-term sustainability and resilience of the food system.

One of the most significant benefits of regenerative agriculture is its ability to improve the health and fertility of the soil. Soil is a vital natural resource that provides the foundation for all plant growth and is essential for producing high-quality crops. Using practices such as cover cropping, composting, and reducing tillage, regenerative agriculture can help increase the amount of organic matter in the soil, leading to improved structure, biology, and nutrient content. This can lead to increased crop yields and improved food security, as well as support the overall health and productivity of the soil.

Another key benefit of regenerative agriculture is the reduction of synthetic inputs such as pesticides and fertilizers.

These inputs can negatively impact the environment, including water pollution and the loss of biodiversity, as well as posing potential risks to human health. By promoting practices such as crop rotation and intercropping, regenerative agriculture can help reduce the need for synthetic inputs and support using natural inputs instead. This can help protect the environment and human health while supporting the food system's long-term sustainability.

In addition to its environmental benefits, regenerative agriculture also has the potential to support the conservation of biodiversity and enhance the resilience of ecosystems to the impacts of climate change. For example, practices such as polycultures, agroforestry, and livestock integration can help increase farm biodiversity and enhance habitat for pollinators and other beneficial insects. This can support the overall health and resilience of the ecosystem while contributing to the food system's long-term sustainability.

Finally, regenerative agriculture has the potential to improve the livelihoods of farmers and create stronger, more sustainable communities. By promoting holistic management and the use of managed grazing, regenerative agriculture can help improve the profitability of farms and create more sustainable and resilient communities. It also recognizes the interconnectedness of all elements of the food system. Therefore, it seeks to create a holistic approach that benefits the environment, farmers, and consumers. By shifting towards regenerative agriculture, we can create a more sustainable and equitable food system for the future.

In conclusion, regenerative agriculture is a holistic and sustainable approach to farming and land management that has the potential to create a more resilient and equitable food system. By focusing on the principles of sustainability, resilience, and regenerative capacity, regenerative agriculture seeks to restore and enhance the health and fertility of the soil, as well as the biodiversity of the ecosystem. The benefits of regenerative agriculture include improved soil health, water conservation, reduced reliance on synthetic inputs, enhanced biodiversity, and improved farmer livelihoods. However, challenges and barriers to adopting regenerative agriculture include a lack of knowledge and resources, limited market demand, regulatory barriers, and cultural and social barriers. To overcome these challenges, investing in education and training programs, research and development, policy and regulatory reform, and market development and support will be important. By working together and implementing regenerative agriculture practices, we can create a more sustainable and equitable food system for the future.

CHAPTER 1
THE PRINCIPLES OF REGENERATIVE AGRICULTURE

The principles of regenerative agriculture are the foundation upon which these systems are built. This chapter will delve into the specific practices that make up these principles, starting with soil health and fertility and moving on to water management, biodiversity, crop rotation and intercropping, and livestock management. Understanding these principles and how they work together is essential for the success of regenerative agriculture systems, as they provide the foundation for sustainable and productive farming practices that benefit the environment, farmers, and consumers.

SOIL HEALTH AND FERTILITY

Regenerative agriculture recognizes that soil is a living, dynamic ecosystem essential to the health and productivity of the entire food system. By focusing on soil health and fertility, regenerative agriculture seeks to create a closed-loop system in which waste is minimized, and resources are used efficiently.

This includes not only the nutrients and water needed for plant growth but also the biological diversity of the soil, which plays a vital role in the ecosystem's overall health.

In addition to providing the necessary nutrients and water for plant growth, healthy soil also can sequester carbon from the atmosphere. Carbon sequestration is capturing and storing carbon dioxide from the atmosphere in the form of organic matter in the soil. This can help mitigate climate change's impacts, as carbon dioxide is a major contributor to global warming. By increasing the amount of organic matter in the soil through practices such as cover cropping and the application of compost, regenerative agriculture can help to increase soil carbon sequestration and combat climate change.

However, industrial agriculture practices often compromise soil health and fertility, which rely on monoculture, synthetic inputs such as pesticides and fertilizers, and large-scale mechanization. These practices can lead to soil erosion, nutrient depletion, and a decline in the biological diversity of the soil. By shifting towards regenerative agriculture practices that prioritize soil health and fertility, it is possible to reverse this trend and create a more sustainable and resilient food system.

In conclusion, soil health and fertility are essential for producing high-quality crops and the overall sustainability of the food system. By focusing on these principles, regenerative agriculture can create a more sustainable and resilient food system that benefits the environment and the people who depend on it.

WATER MANAGEMENT

Water management is an important aspect of regenerative agriculture, as it seeks to conserve this vital resource while maximizing its use in crop production. You can implement several strategies to achieve these goals, including mulching, contour planting, and porous surfaces. These practices help reduce erosion and improve water use efficiency in the farm system.

Rainwater harvesting is another key strategy in water management in regenerative agriculture. By collecting and storing rainwater, farmers can have a reliable source of water for their crops, reducing the need for irrigation and other external water sources. This can be particularly important in regions with scarce water or drought conditions.

Greywater reuse is another water management strategy you can implement in regenerative agriculture. Greywater is wastewater from household activities such as washing dishes, laundry, and showers. It can be collected and treated for reuse in irrigation. This helps reduce the demand for freshwater, a limited and valuable resource. By using greywater in irrigation, farmers can save water and reduce the impact of their farming practices on the environment.

Overall, water management is a critical component of regenerative agriculture, as it helps to conserve this vital resource and improve the efficiency of its use in crop production. By implementing mulching, contour planting, rainwater harvesting, and greywater reuse strategies, farmers can create a more sustainable and resilient food system that benefits both the environment and their livelihoods.

BIODIVERSITY

Biodiversity is the variety of different species that live within an ecosystem. It is a vital component of a healthy and functioning ecosystem. Therefore, regenerative agriculture practices prioritize the conservation of biodiversity to enhance the overall health and resilience of the ecosystem.

One way regenerative agriculture supports biodiversity is by using polycultures, which are diverse plantings that include various crop species. Polycultures can mimic the diversity of natural ecosystems and provide multiple benefits, including increased pest control, improved soil health, and increased water retention.

Agroforestry is another regenerative agriculture practice that supports biodiversity. This practice involves integrating trees and other woody plants into agricultural landscapes, creating a mosaic of different land uses that provide habitat for a wide range of species.

Integrating livestock into regenerative agriculture systems can also support biodiversity by providing a source of organic matter for the soil and improving the land's overall health and fertility. Managed grazing, in particular, can support biodiversity by mimicking the natural movements of wild herds, which can help promote the ecosystem's health.

Overall, regenerative agriculture practices that prioritize biodiversity can help create a more sustainable and resilient food system that benefits the environment and the people who depend on it.

CROP ROTATION AND INTERCROPPING

Crop rotation is a key regenerative agriculture practice involving systematically planting different crops in a specific sequence on the same land. This practice has numerous benefits for soil health and fertility, as it helps improve the soil's structure, biology, and nutrient content. It can also reduce the incidence of pests and diseases, as different crops have different pest and disease pressures. In addition, crop rotation can enhance the farm's overall productivity, as it allows for a more diverse mix of crops to be grown and harvested.

Intercropping is another regenerative agriculture practice that involves planting different crops in close proximity to each other. This practice can improve soil health and fertility, as it allows for the integration of different types of plants with complementary nutrient requirements. For example, intercropping legumes with non-legumes can help fix nitrogen in the soil, which can benefit the growth of non-legume crops. Intercropping can also help to reduce pest and disease pressures, as the presence of different types of crops can create a more diverse and complex ecosystem that is less conducive to pest and disease outbreaks. In addition, intercropping can enhance the farm's overall productivity, as it allows for the simultaneous production of multiple crops on the same piece of land.

Overall, crop rotation and intercropping are key regenerative agriculture practices that can help to improve soil health and fertility, reduce pests and diseases, and enhance the farm's overall productivity. By incorporating these practices into their farming systems, farmers can work towards a more sustainable and resilient food system that benefits the environment and the people who depend on it.

LIVESTOCK MANAGEMENT

Regenerative agriculture systems often prioritize livestock integration in a way that benefits both the animals and the overall health of the ecosystem. You can achieve this through managed grazing, in which livestock are rotated through different pastures, allowing the grasses and other vegetation to recover and regenerate. This practice can help improve soil health and fertility, reduce erosion, and improve water retention. In addition, manure from well-managed livestock can provide a natural source of nutrients for crops, reducing the need for synthetic fertilizers.

It is important to remember that the integration of livestock into regenerative agriculture systems must be done holistically and responsibly, with the health and well-being of the animals as a top priority. This may involve the use of rotational grazing systems, the provision of clean water and high-quality feed, and the implementation of humane handling practices. Taking a holistic approach to livestock management makes it possible to create a symbiotic relationship between the animals and the ecosystem, in which both thrive.

In conclusion, regenerative agriculture offers a promising approach to farming and land management that has the potential to create a more sustainable and equitable food system for the future. By focusing on principles such as soil health and fertility, water management, biodiversity, crop rotation and intercropping, and livestock management, regenerative agriculture can create a closed-loop system in which waste is minimized, and resources are used efficiently. These practices can help improve the soil's health and fertility, conserve water and reduce erosion, enhance biodiversity, and create a more resilient and sustainable food system. In addition, regenerative agriculture has the potential to improve the livelihoods of farmers and create stronger, more sustainable communities. By incorporating these principles and practices into our farming and land management systems, we can work towards a brighter future for agriculture and the environment.

CHAPTER SUMMARY

- The principles of regenerative agriculture include soil health and fertility, water management, biodiversity, crop rotation and intercropping, and livestock management.
- Soil health and fertility are essential for plant growth and carbon sequestration. Industrial agriculture practices often compromise soil health, but regenerative agriculture practices can reverse this trend.
- Water management in regenerative agriculture aims to conserve and efficiently use water through mulching, contour planting, and rainwater harvesting.
- Biodiversity is important for the overall health of the ecosystem. We can promote it through practices such as cover cropping and intercropping.
- Crop rotation and intercropping can improve soil health and fertility and reduce the need for synthetic inputs.
- Livestock management in regenerative agriculture focuses on the welfare of the animals and promoting practices such as rotational grazing.
- Regenerative agriculture can benefit the environment, farmers, and consumers by creating a closed-loop system that minimizes waste and increases resource efficiency.
- The principles of regenerative agriculture work together to create a sustainable and productive farming system.

CHAPTER 2
THE HISTORY OF REGENERATIVE AGRICULTURE

T he history of agriculture is long and complex, with the evolution of farming practices reflecting societies' changing needs and priorities over time. In this chapter, we will explore the history of regenerative agriculture, starting with traditional agricultural practices, followed by the rise of industrial agriculture, and ending with the emergence of regenerative agriculture as a response to the negative impacts of industrial agriculture and the need for a more sustainable food system. By understanding the history of regenerative agriculture, we can gain insights into the challenges and opportunities ahead as we work towards a more sustainable and equitable food system.

TRADITIONAL AGRICULTURAL PRACTICES

Traditional agricultural practices are those that have been passed down through generations and are rooted in the knowledge and wisdom of local communities. These practices are often closely tied to a given community's cultural and social traditions. As a result, they can vary widely depending on the region and the specific needs and conditions of the farm.

One common feature of traditional agricultural practices is using natural inputs, such as compost and animal manure, to enhance soil health and fertility. Compost is made from organic material that has been decomposed and is rich in nutrients and microbial life, which can improve the structure, biology, and nutrient content of the soil. Similarly, animal manure can be a valuable source of nutrients for the soil and provide organic matter that can improve the structure and water-holding capacity of the soil.

In addition to using natural inputs, traditional agricultural practices often involve techniques such as crop rotation and intercropping to enhance soil fertility and productivity. Crop rotation involves planting different crops in a specific order on the same piece of land. In contrast, intercropping involves the planting of different crops near each other. These practices can help improve soil health and fertility by adding nutrients and organic matter to the soil and reducing pests and diseases.

Overall, traditional agricultural practices offer a valuable source of knowledge and wisdom for modern agriculture, as they are based on the principles of sustainability and the understanding that the soil's health is essential for producing high-quality crops. By incorporating these practices into modern agriculture systems, it is possible to create a more sustainable and resilient food system that benefits the environment and the people who depend on it.

THE RISE OF INDUSTRIAL AGRICULTURE

We can trace the rise of industrial agriculture back to the post-World War II era when technological advances and the increasing demand for food led to the adoption of more intensive and mechanized forms of farming. This approach was based on synthetic inputs such as pesticides and fertilizers, as well as monoculture, the cultivation of a single crop over a large area. While industrial agriculture has contributed to increased food production, it has also negatively impacted the environment and the food system's sustainability. These impacts include soil degradation, water pollution, and biodiversity loss.

One of the main drivers of the rise of industrial agriculture was the increasing demand for food due to population growth and urbanization. As more people moved from rural areas to cities, the demand for food increased, leading to the adoption of more efficient and productive farming practices. In addition, the development of new technologies, such as chemical fertilizers and pesticides, also played a role in the rise of industrial agriculture, as these products promised to increase crop yields and reduce the need for labor.

However, the adoption of industrial agriculture practices has also had negative consequences. The reliance on synthetic inputs such as pesticides and fertilizers can lead to soil degradation, as these products can strip the soil of nutrients and disrupt the natural balance of the ecosystem. In addition, the use of monoculture can lead to the loss of biodiversity, as it relies on the cultivation of a single crop over a large area rather than a diverse array of crops. This can make the farm system more vulnerable to pests and diseases, as well as the impacts of climate change.

Overall, the rise of industrial agriculture has contributed to increased food production. Still, it has also negatively impacted the environment and the food system's sustainability. To address these challenges, we must shift towards more sustainable and regenerative practices, such as those in regenerative agriculture.

THE EMERGENCE OF REGENERATIVE AGRICULTURE

Regenerative agriculture is a holistic approach to farming and land management that aims to restore and enhance the health and fertility of the soil, as well as the biodiversity of the ecosystem. It is based on sustainability, resilience, and regenerative capacity principles. It seeks to create a closed-loop system in which waste is minimized and resources are used efficiently. Many different practices and techniques fall under the umbrella of regenerative agriculture, including cover cropping, composting, crop rotation, intercropping, agroforestry, and managed grazing, among others. These practices are often integrated and customized to suit the specific needs and conditions of a given farm or region.

One of the key goals of regenerative agriculture is to improve the health and fertility of the soil. Soil is a vital natural resource that provides the foundation for all plant growth and is essential for producing high-quality crops. Unfortunately, many modern farming practices have degraded the soil, leading to decreased crop yields and increased reliance on synthetic inputs such as fertilizers and pesticides. Regenerative agriculture seeks to reverse this trend by using practices that enhance the soil's structure, biology, and nutrient content, such as cover cropping, composting, and reducing tillage.

In addition to improving soil health, regenerative agriculture also seeks to conserve water and reduce erosion, enhance biodiversity, and integrate livestock in a way that benefits the ecosystem's overall health. These practices can help create a more sustainable and resilient food system that can adapt and thrive in the face of challenges such as climate change and population growth.

Overall, regenerative agriculture offers a promising approach to farming and land management that has the potential to create a more sustainable and equitable food system for the future. By incorporating these principles and practices into our farming and land management systems, we can work towards a brighter future for agriculture and the environment and create a world in which food is produced in a way that is environmentally responsible, socially just, and economically viable.

CHAPTER SUMMARY

- The history of agriculture reflects changing needs and priorities over time, including the emergence of regenerative agriculture.
- Traditional agricultural practices are rooted in local knowledge and wisdom and often involve using natural inputs and techniques such as crop rotation and intercropping to enhance soil health and fertility.
- The rise of industrial agriculture was driven by population growth, urbanization, and technological advances but has negatively impacted the environment and sustainability.
- Industrial agriculture relies on synthetic inputs such as pesticides and fertilizers, monoculture, and large-scale mechanization.
- The negative impacts of industrial agriculture include soil degradation, water pollution, and biodiversity loss.
- The emergence of regenerative agriculture is a response to the negative impacts of industrial agriculture and the need for a more sustainable food system.
- Regenerative agriculture practices focus on soil health and fertility, water management, biodiversity, crop rotation and intercropping, and livestock management.
- Understanding the history of regenerative agriculture can provide insights into the challenges

and opportunities of creating a more sustainable and equitable food system.

CHAPTER 3

THE ENVIRONMENTAL BENEFITS OF REGENERATIVE AGRICULTURE

Regenerative agriculture is not only a sustainable approach to farming but also offers numerous environmental benefits. In this chapter, we will explore the specific environmental benefits of regenerative agriculture, including soil carbon sequestration, water conservation, pesticide and fertilizer reduction, and biodiversity conservation. Furthermore, by understanding how these practices can support the health and resilience of the ecosystem, we can gain insights into the potential for regenerative agriculture to create a more sustainable and equitable food system for the future.

SOIL CARBON SEQUESTRATION

Soil carbon sequestration is a critical aspect of regenerative agriculture, as it addresses the issue of excess carbon dioxide in the atmosphere, which is a major contributor to global warming. Carbon dioxide is a greenhouse gas that traps heat in the atmosphere, increasing the Earth's surface temperature. While carbon dioxide is a naturally occurring gas essential for life on Earth, burning fossil fuels and other human activities have contributed to an excess of this gas in the atmosphere, leading to climate change.

One way to address this excess of carbon dioxide is through carbon sequestration, which captures and stores carbon dioxide in the form of organic matter in the soil. Soil is a natural sponge that can absorb and store carbon dioxide, and regenerative agriculture practices can help to increase the amount of carbon stored in the soil. This is achieved through practices such as cover cropping and applying compost, which add organic matter to the soil and improve its structure and fertility.

In addition to the environmental benefits of carbon sequestration, there are also economic benefits for farmers. Carbon sequestration can increase the value of soil, as it is a valuable resource that we can trade on carbon markets. This can provide an additional source of income for farmers and encourage the adoption of regenerative agriculture practices.

Overall, soil carbon sequestration is a key aspect of regenerative agriculture, as it offers a way to address the issue of climate change and improve the health and fertility of the soil. By focusing on carbon sequestration and other regenerative agriculture practices, we can work towards a more sustainable and resilient food system that benefits the environment and the people who depend on it.

WATER CONSERVATION

Water conservation is essential for the long-term sustainability of agriculture, as it helps to reduce the demand for limited water resources and the associated environmental impacts of irrigation. In many parts of the world, water scarcity is a growing concern. In addition, population growth and climate change are increasing water demand. At the same time, supplies are being strained by drought and other factors. By adopting regenerative agriculture practices that prioritize water conservation, farmers can help to mitigate these challenges and create a more resilient and sustainable food system.

One of the key strategies for water conservation in regenerative agriculture is the use of mulching. Mulching involves the application of a layer of organic material, such as straw or wood chips, to the surface of the soil. This helps to retain moisture in the soil and reduce evaporation, as well as reducing erosion and the need for irrigation. Mulching can also improve the structure and fertility of the soil, as the organic material breaks down and adds nutrients and organic matter to the soil.

Contour planting is another water conservation strategy we can use in regenerative agriculture. This involves planting crops on the contour lines of a slope rather than in straight rows to reduce erosion and improve water use efficiency. By planting on the contour lines, water can flow down the slope in a more controlled manner, reducing erosion and the loss of soil and nutrients. Contour planting can also help improve the farm's overall productivity, as it maximizes the use of available water resources.

Using permeable surfaces is another water conservation strategy we can implement in regenerative agriculture. Permeable surfaces allow water to pass through them rather than running off or being absorbed into the ground. As a result, these surfaces can be used in driveways, paths, and patios. In addition, they can help reduce erosion and the need for irrigation by allowing water to infiltrate the soil. This can be particularly useful in scarce water, as it allows farmers to make the most efficient use of available water resources.

Rainwater harvesting is another key strategy for water conservation in regenerative agriculture. By collecting and storing rainwater, farmers can have a reliable source of water for their crops, reducing the need for irrigation and other external water sources. This can be particularly important in regions with scarce water or drought conditions. We can use various systems for rainwater harvesting, including simple systems such as cisterns or barrels that collect rainwater from rooftops to more complex systems that involve underground reservoirs or pond systems. In addition to providing a water source for irrigation, rainwater harvesting can also help reduce the demand for municipal water systems and improve the farm's overall efficiency of water use.

Greywater reuse is another water conservation strategy we can implement in regenerative agriculture. Greywater is wastewater from household activities such as washing dishes, laundry, and showers. It can be collected and treated for reuse in irrigation. This helps reduce the demand for freshwater, a limited and valuable resource. By using greywater in irrigation, farmers can save water and reduce the impact of their farming practices on the environment. However, it is important to properly treat and filter greywater to ensure that it is safe for irrigation and does not pose any health risks.

Overall, water conservation is an important aspect of regenerative agriculture, as it helps to conserve this vital resource and improve the efficiency of water use on the farm. Furthermore, by implementing strategies such as rainwater harvesting and greywater reuse, farmers can reduce their reliance on external water sources and contribute to the overall sustainability of the food system.

PESTICIDE AND FERTILIZER REDUCTION

One of the main goals of regenerative agriculture is to minimize synthetic inputs, such as pesticides and fertilizers, which can negatively impact the environment and human health. These inputs can pollute water sources and contribute to biodiversity loss, as they can harm beneficial insects and other wildlife. In contrast, regenerative agriculture practices aim to improve the soil's health and fertility through natural inputs and techniques such as crop rotation and intercropping. By enhancing the biology and nutrient content of the soil, regenerative agriculture can help to reduce the need for synthetic inputs and create a more sustainable and resilient food system.

Using natural inputs, such as compost and animal manure, can help improve soil health and fertility by adding nutrients and organic matter to the soil. These inputs also support the growth of beneficial microorganisms, which can improve the structure and biological diversity of the soil. In addition, crop rotation and intercropping can help to improve soil fertility and productivity by adding nutrients and organic matter, as well as reducing pests and diseases. By adopting these practices, farmers can create a more sustainable and resilient food system that can withstand the impacts of climate change and other challenges.

Overall, reducing synthetic inputs, such as pesticides and fertilizers, is a key goal of regenerative agriculture. Instead, by adopting practices that enhance soil health and fertility, farmers can create a more sustainable and resilient food system that benefits the environment and the people who depend on it.

BIODIVERSITY CONSERVATION

Regenerative agriculture practices support farm biodiversity and contribute to biodiversity conservation in the broader landscape. This is because regenerative agriculture systems often rely on a diverse range of crops and animals rather than monoculture, which can help to support a greater variety of species. In addition, regenerative agriculture practices such as cover cropping and agroforestry can provide habitat and food for wildlife, further contributing to biodiversity conservation.

The importance of biodiversity goes beyond the farm, as it plays a vital role in the overall health and functioning of the ecosystem. Biodiversity helps to maintain the balance of nature, as different species interact and support each other in various ways. For example, pollinators such as bees and butterflies play a critical role in the reproduction of many plants. At the same time, predators help to control pest populations. By promoting biodiversity on the farm, regenerative agriculture can help support the ecosystem's overall health and resilience.

Furthermore, biodiversity conservation is important to climate change adaptation and mitigation. As the climate changes, species will need to adapt to survive. Biodiversity can increase the resilience of ecosystems to climate change, as a diverse range of species is more likely to be able to adapt to changing conditions. By promoting biodiversity, regenerative agriculture can help increase the ecosystem's resilience to the impacts of climate change.

In conclusion, biodiversity conservation is a key environmental benefit of regenerative agriculture. By promoting a diverse range of crops and animals and enhancing habitat for pollinators and other beneficial insects, regenerative agriculture can help increase farm biodiversity and the broader land-scape. This, in turn, can help support the overall health and resilience of the ecosystem and contribute to climate change adaptation and mitigation.

In conclusion, regenerative agriculture offers a promising approach to farming and land management that has the potential to create a more sustainable and equitable food system for the future. By incorporating the principles and practices of regenerative agriculture, including soil health and fertility, water management, biodiversity conservation, and the reduction of synthetic inputs, farmers and land managers can work towards a brighter future for agriculture and the environment. In addition to the environmental benefits of regenerative agriculture, there are also economic benefits for farmers, as these practices can improve the productivity and profitability of their operations. By shifting towards regenerative agriculture, we can create a food system that is sustainable, resilient, and equitable for all.

CHAPTER SUMMARY

- Regenerative agriculture has numerous environmental benefits, including soil carbon sequestration, water conservation, pesticide and fertilizer reduction, and biodiversity conservation.
- Soil carbon sequestration captures and stores carbon dioxide in the form of organic matter in the soil, which can help mitigate climate change and improve soil health and fertility.
- Water conservation in regenerative agriculture involves strategies such as mulching and contour planting to reduce the demand for irrigation and improve water use efficiency.
- Pesticide and fertilizer reduction in regenerative agriculture is achieved through cover cropping and intercropping, which can reduce the need for synthetic inputs and improve soil health and fertility.
- Biodiversity conservation in regenerative agriculture is achieved through cover cropping and intercropping practices, which promote a diverse ecosystem and can improve soil health and fertility.
- The environmental benefits of regenerative agriculture can contribute to a more sustainable and equitable food system.
- Regenerative agriculture practices work together to create a closed-loop system that minimizes waste and maximizes resource efficiency.
- By understanding the environmental benefits of regenerative agriculture, we can gain insights into

the potential for this approach to create a more
sustainable and resilient food system.

CHAPTER 4

THE ECONOMIC BENEFITS OF REGENERATIVE AGRICULTURE

I n addition to its environmental benefits, regenerative agriculture offers numerous economic benefits for farmers and communities. This chapter will explore how regenerative agriculture can increase efficiency and productivity, reduce input costs, enhance profitability, and support community development. By understanding the economic benefits of these practices, we can gain insights into the potential for regenerative agriculture to create more sustainable and equitable food systems.

INCREASED EFFICIENCY AND PRODUCTIVITY

Regenerative agriculture practices can improve the efficiency of water use on the farm. By using strategies such as mulching, contour planting, and rainwater harvesting, farmers can reduce the need for irrigation and other external water sources while conserving this vital resource. This can reduce production costs and increase the farm's overall profitability.

In addition to increasing efficiency and productivity, regenerative agriculture practices can also improve the quality of the crops produced. By focusing on soil health and fertility, farmers can produce healthier and more nutrient-dense crops, which can fetch a higher price in the market. This can provide an additional source of income for the farm and help increase the business's overall profitability.

Overall, the increased efficiency and productivity resulting from regenerative agriculture practices can provide various economic benefits for farmers. By shifting towards these practices, farmers can improve the profitability of their operations while also reducing costs and improving the overall sustainability of their farming practices.

REDUCED INPUT COSTS

Regenerative agriculture practices can also reduce input costs by reducing the need for irrigation. Water is a vital resource for agriculture, and the cost of irrigation can be a significant burden for farmers, particularly in areas where water is scarce or subject to drought conditions. By adopting regenerative agriculture practices that prioritize water conservation, such as rainwater harvesting and greywater use, farmers can reduce their reliance on irrigation and save on water costs.

In addition to reducing the costs of synthetic inputs and irrigation, regenerative agriculture practices can also help reduce labor costs. For example, many regenerative agriculture practices, such as cover cropping and mulch, can help suppress weeds, reducing the need for manual labor in the field. This can help to lower labor costs and increase the efficiency and productivity of the farm.

Overall, the potential to reduce input costs is an important economic benefit of regenerative agriculture, as it can help improve the farm's profitability and make it more financially sustainable in the long run. In addition, by adopting these practices, farmers can reduce their production costs and increase their operations' efficiency and productivity.

INCREASED PROFITABILITY

Regenerative agriculture can not only provide economic benefits for farmers, but it can also contribute to the overall sustainability and resilience of the food system. By improving the health and fertility of the soil and reducing the reliance on synthetic inputs, regenerative agriculture practices can create a more sustainable and resilient food system that is better able to withstand the challenges of a changing climate and shifting markets.

One way regenerative agriculture can increase profitability for farmers is through selling high-quality, sustainably-produced foods. Consumers are increasingly seeking out foods produced using sustainable practices and are willing to pay a premium for these products. By adopting regenerative agriculture practices, farmers can differentiate their products and capture a larger market share, leading to increased profits.

In addition to the sale of high-quality foods, regenerative agriculture can also provide economic benefits through the sale of carbon credits. Carbon sequestration, one of the key environmental benefits of regenerative agriculture, can also generate income for farmers. By sequestering carbon in the soil, farmers can participate in carbon markets and sell carbon credits to offset the greenhouse gas emissions of other industries. This can provide an additional source of income for farmers and further encourage the adoption of regenerative agriculture practices.

Overall, regenerative agriculture offers numerous economic benefits for farmers, including increased efficiency and productivity, reduced input costs, and increased profitability. Moreover, by adopting these practices, farmers can not only improve the sustainability and resilience of their farms but also contribute to the overall sustainability and resilience of the food system.

COMMUNITY DEVELOPMENT

In addition to creating economic opportunities for farmers, regenerative agriculture can also support community development by creating more sustainable and equitable food systems. For example, local food production and distribution can help reduce the distance between where food is grown and consumed, reducing the carbon emissions associated with transportation and storage. This can also help to support the local economy, as farmers can sell their products directly to consumers in their community.

Regenerative agriculture can also support community development by promoting social and environmental justice. By prioritizing soil and ecosystem health, regenerative agriculture can help protect the environment and the rights of marginalized communities. For example, by reducing synthetic inputs such as pesticides and fertilizers, regenerative agriculture can help protect the health of farm workers and the surrounding community.

Overall, regenerative agriculture can play a vital role in supporting community development by creating economic opportunities, promoting sustainable and equitable food systems, and protecting the environment and the rights of marginalized communities. By focusing on these principles, it is possible to create more resilient and sustainable communities for the future.

In conclusion, regenerative agriculture offers numerous economic benefits for farmers and communities. By increasing efficiency and productivity, reducing input costs, and enhancing profitability, regenerative agriculture practices can help to create more sustainable and equitable food systems. In addition to these benefits, regenerative agriculture can also support community development by creating new jobs and revitalizing local food systems. As more and more farmers adopt these practices, the economic benefits of regenerative agriculture will become increasingly apparent, making it a viable and valuable option for the future of agriculture.

CHAPTER SUMMARY

- Regenerative agriculture offers numerous economic benefits for farmers and communities, including increased efficiency and productivity, reduced input costs, enhanced profitability, and support for community development.
- Increased efficiency and productivity in regenerative agriculture are achieved through mulching and contour planting, which can reduce the need for irrigation and improve crop quality.
- Reduced input costs in regenerative agriculture are achieved through rainwater harvesting and greywater use, which reduce the need for irrigation and cover cropping, which reduces the need for labor.
- We can achieve increased profitability in regenerative agriculture by selling high-quality, sustainably-produced foods and carbon credits.
- Support for community development in regenerative agriculture is achieved through community-supported agriculture, which connects farmers and consumers, and agroforestry, which provides economic and social benefits for local communities.
- The economic benefits of regenerative agriculture can contribute to a more sustainable and equitable food system.
- By understanding the economic benefits of regenerative agriculture, we can gain insights into

the potential for this approach to create a more
sustainable and resilient food system.

- The economic benefits of regenerative agriculture
  work together with the environmental benefits to
  create a more sustainable and productive farming
  system.

CHAPTER 5
THE SOCIAL BENEFITS OF REGENERATIVE AGRICULTURE

Regenerative agriculture not only offers environmental and economic benefits but also has the potential to enhance social well-being and contribute to creating more equitable food systems. In this chapter, we will explore the specific social benefits of regenerative agriculture, including improved public health, enhanced rural livelihoods, increased food security, and strengthened communities. By understanding how these practices can support social well-being, we can gain insights into the potential for regenerative agriculture to create a more sustainable and equitable food system for the future.

IMPROVED PUBLIC HEALTH

Regenerative agriculture has the potential to improve public health in several ways significantly. Firstly, by reducing the reliance on synthetic inputs such as pesticides and fertilizers, regenerative agriculture practices can help to protect both the environment and human health. These inputs are often associated with negative impacts on ecosystems and human health, including the contamination of water sources and the development of chronic diseases. By replacing these inputs with natural alternatives and emphasizing soil health, regenerative agriculture can help to create a healthier and more sustainable food system.

In addition to reducing the negative impacts of synthetic inputs, regenerative agriculture can improve dietary health by producing nutrient-rich, locally-grown foods. These foods are often fresher and more nutrient-dense than those grown using conventional methods, which can positively impact consumers' health. For example, research has shown that locally-grown, nutrient-rich foods can help to reduce the risk of diet-related diseases such as obesity and heart disease.

Furthermore, regenerative agriculture practices can also support the development of community gardens and other forms of local food production, which can help to increase access to healthy, affordable foods for underserved communities. This can be particularly important in areas where access to fresh, nutritious foods is limited, as it can help to address food insecurity and improve overall health outcomes.

Overall, the improved public health resulting from regenerative agriculture is an important social benefit of these practices. By reducing the negative impacts of synthetic inputs, promoting the production of nutrient-rich foods, and supporting local food systems, regenerative agriculture can help to create a healthier and more sustainable food system for all.

ENHANCED RURAL LIVELIHOODS

Regenerative agriculture has the potential to significantly enhance rural livelihoods by providing economic opportunities for farmers and creating more sustainable and equitable food systems. By focusing on the health and fertility of the soil and reducing the reliance on synthetic inputs, regenerative agriculture practices can improve the efficiency and productivity of farming operations, leading to increased profitability for farmers. In addition, adopting regenerative agriculture practices can also reduce input costs, such as irrigation and labor, which can further improve the financial sustainability of farming operations.

In addition to the economic benefits of regenerative agriculture for farmers, these practices can also support the development of local food systems and enhance rural livelihoods in other ways. For example, by supporting local food production and distribution, regenerative agriculture can help to create more resilient and sustainable communities. This can be particularly important in rural areas where access to fresh, nutritious foods is limited, as it can help to address food insecurity and improve overall health outcomes.

Furthermore, regenerative agriculture practices can also create new economic opportunities for farmers, such as producing and selling high-quality, sustainably-grown foods. As consumers become increasingly interested in the sustainability of their food choices, a growing demand for products produced using regenerative agriculture practices is growing. As a result, farmers can differentiate their products by meeting this demand and capturing a larger market share, increasing profits.

Overall, the enhanced rural livelihoods resulting from

regenerative agriculture are an important social benefit of these practices. By providing economic opportunities for farmers and supporting the development of local food systems, regenerative agriculture can help to create more sustainable and equitable communities.

INCREASED FOOD SECURITY

Increasing food security is an important social benefit of regenerative agriculture. By improving the health and fertility of the soil, regenerative agriculture practices can lead to increased crop yields and enhanced food production. This can be particularly important in areas where food insecurity is a major issue, as it can help to address shortages and ensure that communities have access to a reliable source of nutritious food.

One way regenerative agriculture can increase food security is through techniques such as crop rotation and intercropping. These practices can help improve the farm's overall efficiency and productivity by increasing the diversity of crops grown and enhancing the health of the soil. Crop rotation, in particular, can help to reduce the risk of soil degradation and improve the overall sustainability of the farm, as it allows farmers to alternate between different crops and rest the soil between growing seasons. This can help to maintain soil health and fertility over time, leading to increased crop yields and improved food security.

In addition to increasing crop yields and improving the efficiency and productivity of the farm, regenerative agriculture practices can also help to increase food security by promoting local food systems. By supporting the production and distribution of locally-grown foods, regenerative agriculture can help to reduce the reliance on imported foods and create more resilient and sustainable communities. This can be particularly important in areas where access to fresh, nutritious foods is limited, as it can help to address food insecurity and improve overall health outcomes.

Overall, the increased food security resulting from regenerative agriculture is an important social benefit of these practices. By improving the soil's health and fertility, enhancing the farm's efficiency and productivity, and promoting local food systems, regenerative agriculture can help ensure that communities have access to a reliable source of nutritious food.

STRENGTHENED COMMUNITIES

Regenerative agriculture has the potential to significantly strengthen communities by promoting local food production and distribution and by supporting the development of more resilient and sustainable communities. In addition, by focusing on the health and fertility of the soil and reducing the reliance on synthetic inputs, regenerative agriculture practices can improve the efficiency and productivity of farming operations, leading to increased profitability for farmers. This can create new economic opportunities and support the development of local food systems, which can contribute to the overall wellbeing of communities.

In addition to the economic benefits of regenerative agriculture for farmers, these practices can also support the development of more resilient and sustainable communities in other ways. For example, by promoting local food production and distribution, regenerative agriculture can help to reduce the reliance on imported foods and create more self-sufficient communities. This can be particularly important in areas where access to fresh, nutritious foods is limited, as it can help to address food insecurity and improve overall health outcomes.

Furthermore, regenerative agriculture practices can also contribute to the social well-being of communities by providing opportunities for education and collaboration. For example, by supporting the development of community gardens and other forms of local food production, regenerative agriculture can create opportunities for people to come together and learn from one another. This can help to build social connections and promote a sense of community, which can contribute to overall well-being.

Overall, the strengthened communities resulting from regenerative agriculture are an important social benefit of these practices. By promoting local food production and distribution, supporting the development of more resilient and sustainable communities, and enhancing social well-being, regenerative agriculture can help to create more equitable and sustainable food systems.

In summary, regenerative agriculture offers numerous social benefits that can positively impact the environment, farmers, and consumers. By focusing on the health and fertility of the soil and reducing the reliance on synthetic inputs, regenerative agriculture practices can improve the efficiency and productivity of farming operations, leading to increased profitability for farmers and enhanced rural livelihoods. In addition, regenerative agriculture can improve public health by producing nutrient-rich, locally-grown foods and reducing the negative impacts of synthetic inputs. These practices can also support the development of local food systems and increase food security, helping to ensure that communities have access to a reliable source of nutritious food. Finally, regenerative agriculture can strengthen communities by promoting local food production and distribution and supporting the development of more resilient and sustainable communities.

Overall, by incorporating the principles of regenerative agriculture into farming and land management practices, it is possible to create a more sustainable and equitable food system that benefits all stakeholders. By prioritizing the health and fertility of the soil and by reducing the reliance on synthetic inputs, regenerative agriculture can help to create a food system that is more resilient, productive, and sustainable in the long run.

CHAPTER SUMMARY

- Regenerative agriculture can improve public health by reducing the reliance on synthetic inputs, producing nutrient-rich, locally-grown foods, and supporting community gardens and local food systems.
- These practices can enhance rural livelihoods by providing economic opportunities for farmers, creating more sustainable and equitable food systems, and supporting local food production and distribution.
- Regenerative agriculture can increase food security by supporting local food systems and increasing the availability of nutrient-rich foods.
- These practices can also strengthen communities by promoting social connections, supporting cultural traditions, and fostering a sense of place and identity.
- To realize the social benefits of regenerative agriculture, we must adopt a holistic approach that considers the needs and priorities of different stakeholders, including farmers, consumers, and the broader community.
- Policy and regulatory frameworks can support the adoption of regenerative agriculture practices as an education and outreach effort.
- Public-private partnerships and other forms of collaboration can also be useful in promoting the adoption and scaling of regenerative agriculture practices.

- To achieve regenerative agriculture's social, environmental, and economic benefits, we must adopt a systems-level approach that considers the interconnectedness of different factors and stakeholders in the food system.

CHAPTER 6

CHALLENGES AND BARRIERS TO IMPLEMENTING REGENERATIVE AGRICULTURE

D espite its numerous benefits, adopting regenerative agriculture practices can be challenging, and several barriers may prevent its widespread implementation. This chapter will explore some of the main challenges and barriers to implementing regenerative agriculture, including lack of knowledge and resources, limited market demand, regulatory barriers, and cultural and social barriers. By understanding these challenges and barriers, we can gain insights into the potential strategies and solutions for promoting the adoption of regenerative agriculture practices.

LACK OF KNOWLEDGE AND RESOURCES

One of the main challenges to the widespread adoption of regenerative agriculture practices is the need for more knowledge and resources among farmers. Many farmers may need to become more familiar with these practices. In addition, they may need access to the necessary information and resources to implement them on their farm. This can be a significant barrier to the adoption of regenerative agriculture, as farmers may be hesitant to adopt new practices without the necessary support and guidance.

In addition to the lack of knowledge and resources, there may also be a need for more training and extension programs to support farmers adopting regenerative agriculture practices. These programs can provide valuable information and resources to farmers, helping them understand the benefits and challenges of regenerative agriculture and providing guidance on implementing these practices on their farms. Without access to these programs, farmers may be less likely to adopt regenerative agriculture practices, even if they are interested in doing so.

Furthermore, the lack of knowledge and resources can also challenge farmers interested in transitioning to regenerative agriculture but need help figuring out where to start. However, with access to the necessary information and resources, farmers may be able to develop a clear plan for implementing these practices on their farms, which can be a significant barrier to the adoption of regenerative agriculture.

The lack of knowledge and resources is a significant challenge to the widespread adoption of regenerative agriculture practices. By providing more information and resources to farmers and supporting the development of training and extension programs, it is possible to overcome this challenge and support the widespread adoption of regenerative agriculture practices.

LIMITED MARKET DEMAND

Limited market demand for sustainably-produced foods is another significant challenge to the widespread adoption of regenerative agriculture practices. While there is growing interest in sustainably-produced foods, more is needed to support the widespread adoption of regenerative agriculture practices. This can be a significant barrier to adopting regenerative agriculture. Farmers may be hesitant to invest in these practices if they are unsure of their ability to sell their products.

One way we can address this challenge is through developing marketing and branding strategies that highlight the benefits of sustainably-produced foods and help differentiate these products from conventionally-grown foods. In addition, promoting the sustainability and quality of sustainably-produced foods may increase consumer demand for these products and create more opportunities for farmers interested in adopting regenerative agriculture practices.

In addition to marketing and branding efforts, there may also be a need for policy changes and other interventions to support the development of a more robust market for sustainably-produced foods. For example, governments and other organizations may need to work to create incentives for the production and purchase of sustainably-grown foods or to support the development of distribution channels for these products. By addressing these challenges and creating a more supportive market environment for sustainably-produced foods, it may be possible to increase the demand for these products and support the widespread adoption of regenerative agriculture practices.

REGULATORY BARRIERS

Regulatory barriers can significantly challenge the implementation of regenerative agriculture practices. For example, certain practices may be restricted by law, or financial incentives or subsidies may support the adoption of industrial agriculture practices rather than regenerative agriculture practices. These regulatory barriers can make it difficult for farmers to adopt regenerative agriculture practices, as they may be hesitant to invest in these practices if they are unsure of their legal status or the availability of financial support.

We can address regulatory barriers by developing policies and regulations supporting regenerative agriculture practices. For example, governments and other organizations may need to work to remove restrictions on these practices or to provide financial incentives or subsidies to farmers who are interested in adopting these practices. By creating a more supportive policy environment for regenerative agriculture, it may be possible to overcome regulatory barriers and encourage the widespread adoption of these practices.

In addition to policy interventions, there is also a need for education and outreach efforts to increase awareness of the benefits of regenerative agriculture and the challenges posed by regulatory barriers. By providing more information to farmers and other stakeholders about the benefits and challenges of these practices, it may be possible to build support for policy changes that support the adoption of regenerative agriculture practices.

Overall, regulatory barriers can significantly challenge the implementation of regenerative agriculture practices. By addressing these barriers through policy changes, education, and outreach efforts, it may be possible to create a more supportive environment for regenerative agriculture and encourage the widespread adoption of these practices. By removing restrictions on regenerative agriculture practices and providing financial incentives and subsidies to farmers interested in adopting these practices, governments and other organizations can help overcome regulatory barriers and support the development of more sustainable and equitable food systems.

CULTURAL AND SOCIAL BARRIERS

Cultural and social barriers can also significantly challenge adopting regenerative agriculture practices. For example, traditional farming practices are deeply ingrained in certain cultures, and there may be resistance to change. This can be a significant barrier to adopting regenerative agriculture practices, as farmers may be hesitant to adopt new practices if they are unfamiliar or perceived as conflicting with traditional ways of farming.

In addition to cultural barriers, there may also be social and economic pressures that discourage the adoption of regenerative agriculture practices. For example, there may be a need to maximize short-term profits, which can lead farmers to prioritize efficiency and productivity over their farming operations' long-term health and sustainability. There may also be a need for more access to capital and other resources, making it difficult for farmers to invest in the equipment and infrastructure needed to implement regenerative agriculture practices.

To overcome these cultural and social barriers, engaging in education and outreach efforts that highlight the benefits of regenerative agriculture and address any concerns or misconceptions about these practices may be necessary. In addition, there may be a need for policy interventions and other support mechanisms to address the social and economic pressures that discourage the adoption of regenerative agriculture practices. However, by addressing these cultural and social barriers and creating a more supportive environment for regenerative agriculture, it may be possible to overcome these challenges and encourage the widespread adoption of these practices.

In summary, there are several challenges and barriers to implementing regenerative agriculture, including a lack of knowledge and resources, limited market demand, regulatory barriers, and cultural and social barriers. Understanding these challenges and barriers makes it possible to identify strategies and solutions for promoting the adoption of regenerative agriculture practices and creating more sustainable and equitable food systems.

CHAPTER SUMMARY

- Lack of knowledge and resources can significantly challenge the widespread adoption of regenerative agriculture practices.
- Limited market demand for sustainably-produced foods can also be a barrier to adoption.
- Regulatory barriers, such as subsidies for synthetic inputs, can discourage the adoption of regenerative agriculture practices.
- Cultural and social barriers, such as traditional farming practices and skepticism towards new approaches, can also hinder adoption.
- Financial barriers, such as the initial investment required to implement regenerative agriculture practices, can challenge farmers.
- Access to land and other resources, such as water, can also be a barrier to adoption.
- Political and economic factors, such as trade policies and market forces, can impact the feasibility of adopting regenerative agriculture practices.
- There needs to be more research and data on the effectiveness of regenerative agriculture practices to make it easier for farmers to make informed decisions about adoption.

CHAPTER 7
SOLUTIONS AND STRATEGIES FOR OVERCOMING CHALLENGES

espite the numerous challenges and barriers to implementing regenerative agriculture, we can employ a range of solutions and strategies to overcome these challenges and promote the adoption of these practices. This chapter will explore some of the main solutions and strategies for overcoming challenges to regenerative agriculture, including education and training programs, research and development, policy and regulatory reform, and market development and support. By understanding these strategies and solutions, we can gain insights into the potential for promoting the adoption of regenerative agriculture practices and creating more sustainable and equitable food systems.

EDUCATION AND TRAINING PROGRAMS

Education and training programs are an important solution to the challenge of lack of knowledge and resources when adopting regenerative agriculture practices. Providing farmers with the necessary information and resources, as well as training in these practices, supports the adoption of regenerative agriculture and helps farmers to understand the benefits and challenges of these practices.

There are several types of education and training programs that can be effective in supporting the adoption of regenerative agriculture practices. For example, extension programs can provide valuable information and resources to farmers, as well as technical assistance and guidance on implementing these practices on their farms. In addition, online courses, workshops, and other forms of training can provide farmers with the knowledge and skills they need to understand and implement regenerative agriculture practices.

One of the key benefits of education and training programs is that they can provide farmers with the support they need to overcome the challenges and barriers to adopting regenerative agriculture practices. Providing access to information and resources, as well as guidance and technical assistance, can help farmers feel more confident and capable of implementing these practices on their farms. In addition, education and training programs can also help build a sense of community and support among farmers interested in adopting regenerative agriculture practices, which can be an important factor in helping these practices be more widely adopted.

Overall, education and training programs are a key solution to the challenge of lack of knowledge and resources when adopting regenerative agriculture practices. Providing farmers with the necessary information and resources, as well as training and technical assistance, can support adopting these practices and creating more sustainable and equitable food systems.

RESEARCH AND DEVELOPMENT

Research and development is a critical strategy for overcoming challenges to the widespread adoption of regenerative agriculture practices. Investing in research to improve our understanding of these practices and their impacts makes it possible to develop more effective and sustainable approaches to regenerative agriculture. This research can also help identify the most effective strategies and solutions for promoting the adoption of regenerative agriculture practices and can also provide valuable insights into the challenges and barriers that farmers and other stakeholders may face when implementing these practices.

Several types of research and development can be useful in addressing the challenges to regenerative agriculture. For example, research on these practices' environmental impacts can help identify the most sustainable approaches to regenerative agriculture and provide valuable information about the benefits of these practices for soil health, water conservation, and biodiversity. Research on the economic impacts of these practices can also be useful, as it can help identify the most cost-effective and profitable approaches to regenerative agriculture and provide insights into how these practices can support the development of more sustainable and equitable food systems.

In addition to research on regenerative agriculture's environmental and economic impacts, research on social and cultural issues can also be valuable. For example, research on the cultural and social barriers to adopting these practices can help identify strategies for overcoming these barriers and promoting the widespread adoption of these practices. Investing in research and development makes it possible to gain a more comprehensive understanding of the challenges and opportunities presented by regenerative agriculture and identify the most effective strategies for addressing these challenges and promoting the adoption of these practices.

Overall, research and development is a critical strategy for overcoming the challenges of the widespread adoption of regenerative agriculture practices. Investing in research to improve our understanding of these practices and their impacts makes it possible to develop more effective and sustainable approaches to regenerative agriculture and identify the most effective strategies and solutions for promoting the adoption of these practices.

POLICY AND REGULATORY REFORM

Policy and regulatory reform is a critical strategy for overcoming challenges to the widespread adoption of regenerative agriculture practices. By reforming policies and regulations that support industrial agriculture practices and discourage adopting regenerative agriculture practices, it is possible to create a more supportive environment for these practices. This may include changes to subsidies, incentives, and other financial support mechanisms, as well as changes to laws and regulations that align with the principles of regenerative agriculture.

One of the key benefits of the policy and regulatory reform is that it can create a more level playing field for regenerative agriculture practices, making it easier for farmers to adopt and compete in the marketplace. For example, by providing financial incentives or subsidies to farmers who adopt regenerative agriculture practices, it is possible to make these practices more attractive and economically viable for farmers. In addition, by reforming regulations that support industrial agriculture practices and discourage the adoption of regenerative agriculture practices, it is possible to create a more supportive environment for these practices, encouraging more farmers to adopt them.

Policy and regulatory reform can also include the development of standards and certification programs that recognize and reward the adoption of regenerative agriculture practices. By creating standards and certification programs that reflect the principles of regenerative agriculture, it is possible to create a more transparent and accountable system for recognizing and rewarding the adoption of these practices. This can create a more supportive environment for regenerative agriculture and encourage more farmers to adopt these practices.

Overall, policy and regulatory reform is a key strategy for overcoming challenges to the widespread adoption of regenerative agriculture practices. By reforming policies and regulations that support industrial agriculture practices and discourage the adoption of regenerative agriculture practices, it is possible to create a more supportive environment for these practices and create the conditions for them to thrive and become more widely adopted.

MARKET DEVELOPMENT AND SUPPORT

Market development and support are crucial strategies for overcoming challenges to the widespread adoption of regenerative agriculture practices. Increasing the demand for sustainably-produced foods makes it possible to create a more supportive environment for these practices and encourage more farmers to adopt them.

Several strategies can effectively increase the market

demand for sustainably-produced foods and support the adoption of regenerative agriculture practices. For example, marketing and labeling initiatives can educate consumers about these foods' benefits and the practices used to produce them and create a more attractive and appealing market for these products. Direct-to-consumer sales, such as farmers' markets and community-supported agriculture (CSA) programs, can also increase the demand for sustainably-produced foods and support the adoption of regenerative agriculture practices. In addition, developing local and regional food systems can create more opportunities for farmers to sell their sustainably-produced foods and can help to increase the market demand for these products.

Increasing the market demand for sustainably-produced foods makes it possible to create economic incentives for farmers to adopt regenerative agriculture practices. By providing farmers with more opportunities to sell their sustainably-produced foods and creating a more attractive and appealing market for these products, it is possible to encourage more farmers to adopt these practices and create more sustainable and equitable food systems.

Overall, market development and support are crucial strategies for overcoming challenges to the widespread adoption of regenerative agriculture practices. Increasing the market demand for sustainably-produced foods makes it possible to create economic incentives for farmers to adopt these practices and create more sustainable and equitable food systems.

In conclusion, we can employ various solutions and strategies to overcome the challenges and barriers to implementing regenerative agriculture practices. These include education and training programs, research and development, policy and regulatory reform, and market development and support. Understanding these strategies and solutions makes it possible to identify the most effective approaches for promoting the adoption of regenerative agriculture practices and creating more sustainable and equitable food systems.

CHAPTER SUMMARY

- Education and training programs are a key solution to the lack of knowledge and resources when adopting regenerative agriculture practices.
- Research and development is a critical strategy for improving our understanding of regenerative agriculture practices and developing more effective approaches.
- Policy and regulatory reform can help to create a more supportive environment for regenerative agriculture by promoting sustainable farming practices and supporting farmers interested in adopting these practices.
- Market development and support can help create a more robust market for sustainably-produced foods, increasing demand for these products and supporting the adoption of regenerative agriculture practices.
- Collaboration and partnerships can help build a sense of community and support among farmers and other stakeholders interested in regenerative agriculture, which can be important in promoting and adopting these practices.
- Financing and investment can help provide the necessary resources for farmers to adopt regenerative agriculture practices and support the development of more sustainable and equitable food systems.
- Public awareness and outreach can help increase understanding of regenerative agriculture's benefits

and promote the adoption of these practices by a wider audience.

- Government and other policymakers have an important role in promoting the adoption of regenerative agriculture practices and creating a more sustainable and equitable food system.

CHAPTER 8
THE FUTURE OF REGENERATIVE AGRICULTURE

As the global population continues to grow and the impacts of climate change become more apparent, it is essential to consider regenerative agriculture's role in addressing these challenges and creating a more sustainable and equitable food system. In this chapter, we will explore the potential of regenerative agriculture to address climate change, feed the world, and support government and policy efforts to promote these practices.

THE ROLE OF REGENERATIVE AGRICULTURE IN ADDRESSING CLIMATE CHANGE

Regenerative agriculture has a significant role in addressing the challenges of climate change. One of the key ways in which these practices can contribute to climate change mitigation is through the sequestration of carbon in the soil. Practices such as using cover crops and applying compost can help increase the amount of organic matter in the soil, leading to increased carbon sequestration. This not only helps to mitigate the impacts of climate change but also improves the health and fertility of the soil.

In addition to carbon sequestration, regenerative agriculture practices can contribute to climate change mitigation by reducing greenhouse gas emissions. By reducing the need for synthetic inputs such as pesticides and fertilizers, regenerative agriculture practices can help reduce agriculture's environmental impacts and decrease the release of greenhouse gases. For example, using cover crops and compost can help increase soil health and fertility, reducing the need for synthetic inputs and the emissions associated with their production and use.

Regenerative agriculture practices can also contribute to climate change adaptation by improving the resilience of agricultural systems. By enhancing the health and fertility of the soil, these practices can help to improve the productivity and sustainability of agricultural systems and increase their ability to withstand the impacts of a changing climate. For example, regenerative agriculture practices that focus on soil health and water conservation can help to improve the resilience of agricultural systems in the face of drought and other extreme weather events.

Overall, regenerative agriculture has a significant role in addressing the challenges of climate change. By improving the health and fertility of the soil, reducing greenhouse gas emissions, and enhancing the resilience of agricultural systems, these practices can contribute to creating a more sustainable and equitable food system that is better able to withstand the impacts of a changing climate.

THE POTENTIAL FOR REGENERATIVE AGRICULTURE TO FEED THE WORLD

The potential for regenerative agriculture to feed the world is an important aspect of the future of these practices. While industrial agriculture has succeeded in increasing food production, it has also contributed to environmental degradation and biodiversity loss. In contrast, regenerative agriculture practices can increase food production sustainably and equitably.

One of the key ways in which regenerative agriculture can increase food production is by improving soil health and fertility. By adopting practices such as using cover crops and compost, farmers can improve the quality and fertility of the soil, leading to increased crop yields and improved food security. In addition, regenerative agriculture practices that focus on soil health and fertility can also enhance the resilience of agricultural systems, making them more resistant to the impacts of extreme weather events and other challenges.

Another way in which regenerative agriculture can increase food production is through the conservation of water. By adopting practices such as rainwater harvesting and greywater, farmers can reduce their reliance on irrigation and other external water sources, leading to increased efficiency and productivity. This can help to improve food security and increase the sustainability of agricultural systems.

Overall, the potential for regenerative agriculture to feed the world is significant. Improving soil health and fertility, conserving water, and enhancing ecosystem resilience can increase food production sustainably and equitably. By adopting regenerative agriculture practices, farmers can contribute to creating a more sustainable and equitable food system that can better feed the world's growing population.

THE ROLE OF GOVERNMENT AND POLICY IN SUPPORTING REGENERATIVE AGRICULTURE

The role of government and policy in supporting regenerative agriculture is critical to the widespread adoption and scaling of these practices. Governments and policymakers have several tools to support the adoption and scaling of regenerative agriculture practices, including education and training programs, research and development initiatives, and policy and regulatory reforms.

Education and training programs can be important tools for supporting the adoption of regenerative agriculture practices. Providing farmers with the necessary information and resources, as well as training in these practices, supports the adoption of these practices and creates a more supportive environment for regenerative agriculture. In addition, extension programs and other forms of technical assistance can also effectively provide farmers with the support they need to implement regenerative agriculture practices on their farms.

Research and development initiatives are another important tools for supporting regenerative agriculture adoption. Investing in research to improve our understanding of these practices and their impacts makes it possible to develop more effective and sustainable approaches to regenerative agriculture. This research can also help to identify the most effective strategies and solutions for promoting the adoption of regenerative agriculture practices.

Policy and regulatory reform is another key strategy for supporting the adoption of regenerative agriculture practices.

By reforming policies and regulations that support industrial agriculture practices and discourage adopting regenerative agriculture practices, it is possible to create a more supportive environment for these practices. This may include changes to subsidies, incentives, and other financial support mechanisms, as well as changes to laws and regulations that align with the principles of regenerative agriculture. Policy and regulatory reform can also include the development of standards and certification programs that recognize and reward the adoption of regenerative agriculture practices.

Finally, governments and policymakers can support the development of alternative food systems, such as local and regional food systems, based on the principles of regenerative agriculture. By creating more opportunities for farmers to sell their sustainably-produced foods and by supporting the development of more resilient and sustainable communities, it is possible to create a more supportive environment for regenerative agriculture practices and contribute to creating a more sustainable and equitable food system. Local and regional food systems can increase the market demand for sustainably-produced foods, create economic opportunities for farmers, and enhance the resilience of communities. By investing in the development of alternative food systems, governments and policymakers can help create the necessary conditions for the adoption and scaling of regenerative agriculture practices and contribute to creating a more sustainable and equitable food system.

The future of regenerative agriculture is bright, with the potential to address some of the most pressing challenges facing the world today, including climate change and food security. Focusing on soil health and fertility, water conservation, biodiversity, and other principles of regenerative agriculture makes it possible to create a more sustainable and equitable food system that benefits the environment, farmers, and consumers. The role of government and policy in supporting regenerative agriculture is also crucial, as it can help to create a more supportive environment for these practices and accelerate their adoption. While there are challenges and barriers to the implementation of regenerative agriculture, there is also a range of solutions and strategies that we can employ to overcome these challenges. By working together and sharing knowledge and resources, it is possible to create a brighter future for regenerative agriculture and the food system.

CHAPTER SUMMARY

- Regenerative agriculture can address climate change by sequestering carbon in the soil, reducing greenhouse gas emissions, and enhancing the resilience of agricultural systems.
- Regenerative agriculture has the potential to increase food production sustainably and equitably by improving soil health and fertility, conserving water, and promoting biodiversity.
- Governments and policymakers can support the adoption of regenerative agriculture practices through financial incentives, research and development, and regulatory reform.
- International organizations and NGOs can support the adoption of regenerative agriculture by promoting education and training programs, conducting research and development, and advocating for policy reform.
- Consumers can support the adoption of regenerative agriculture by purchasing sustainably-produced foods, participating in community-supported agriculture programs, and advocating for policy reform.
- The private sector can support the adoption of regenerative agriculture by investing in research and development, promoting sustainable supply chains, and advocating for policy reform.
- Land conservation organizations can support the adoption of regenerative agriculture by promoting education and training programs, conducting

research and development, and advocating for policy reform.

- Universities and other educational institutions can support the adoption of regenerative agriculture by conducting research, promoting education and training programs, and advocating for policy reform.

CONCLUSION

n this book, we have explored the principles and benefits of regenerative agriculture and the challenges and barriers to its implementation. We have examined the role of soil health and fertility, water management, biodiversity, and livestock management in regenerative agriculture and how these practices can improve crop yields, reduce the need for synthetic inputs, enhance ecosystem resilience, and create more sustainable communities. We have also highlighted regenerative agriculture's economic and social benefits, including increased efficiency and productivity, reduced input costs, increased profitability, improved public health, enhanced rural livelihoods, increased food security, and strengthened communities.

We have also discussed the challenges and barriers to implementing regenerative agriculture, including lack of knowledge and resources, limited market demand, regulatory barriers, and cultural and social barriers. Finally, we have explored solutions and strategies for overcoming these challenges, including education and training programs, research and development, policy and regulatory reform, and market development and support.

In the final chapter, we considered the future of regenerative agriculture and the role it can play in addressing climate change and feeding the world. We also explored the importance of government and policy in supporting regenerative agriculture and the potential for these practices to create a more sustainable and equitable food system.

Overall, it is clear that regenerative agriculture offers a promising and holistic approach to farming and land management that has the potential to address many of the challenges facing the food system today. By adopting these practices and working together to overcome challenges and barriers, it is possible to create a brighter future for regenerative agriculture and the food system.

AFTERWORD

In *The Power of Regenerative Agriculture*, we have explored the principles, benefits, and strategies of regenerative agriculture and how this sustainable approach to agriculture can create a more sustainable and equitable future for all.

As we consider the future of agriculture, it is clear that regenerative agriculture has the potential to play a critical role in shaping a more sustainable and resilient food system. From improving soil health and water retention to sequestering carbon and supporting biodiversity, regenerative agriculture offers a holistic approach to addressing some of our planet's most pressing challenges.

But the journey towards a regenerative agriculture future is not without its challenges. From economic and social barriers to cultural and political obstacles, we must overcome many challenges to realize this approach's potential fully. However, as we have seen throughout this book, many solutions and strategies can help us overcome these challenges and create a more sustainable and equitable future.

As we look to the future, it is clear that regenerative agriculture offers a path toward a more sustainable and resilient food system. I hope this book has inspired you to learn more about this transformative approach to agriculture and consider how you can be a part of this important movement. Thank you for joining me on this journey. So, it is our responsibility to take care of the land and use it in a sustainable and regenerative way. Only then can we create a healthy and prosperous future for all.

Sincerely, Michael Barton

ACKNOWLEDGMENTS

I am deeply grateful to the many individuals who have supported and contributed to the creation of this book, *The Power of Regenerative Agriculture*.

I want to thank my colleagues and mentors in sustainable agriculture, who have shared their knowledge and experience with me over the years. Your insights and guidance have been invaluable in shaping my understanding of regenerative agriculture and its potential to create a more sustainable and equitable future.

I would also like to thank my family and friends, who have supported and encouraged me throughout the writing process. Your belief in me has been a constant source of motivation and inspiration.

Finally, I thank the farmers, environmentalists, policymakers, and all working towards a more sustainable and equitable future through regenerative agriculture. Your dedication and hard work are a constant reminder of the importance of this movement and inspire me to do my part in advocating for and supporting it. Thank you for all that you do.

Sincerely, Michael Barton

ABOUT THE AUTHOR

Michael Barton is a sustainability expert with a passion for regenerative agriculture. With over a decade of experience in the field, he has worked with farmers, policymakers, and environmentalists to promote sustainable farming practices and advocate for the adoption of regenerative agriculture.

Michael holds a degree in Environmental Studies and has completed advanced training in regenerative agriculture principles and practices. He has worked with organizations worldwide to promote sustainable agriculture and food systems and has published numerous articles and papers on the subject.

In *The Power of Regenerative Agriculture*, Michael brings together his expertise and experience to offer a comprehensive guide to regenerative agriculture's principles, benefits, and strategies. His passion for sustainability and his belief in the potential of regenerative agriculture to create a more sustainable and equitable future shines through on every page of this important resource.

ABOUT THE AUTHOR

FROM THE AUTHOR

Dear Reader,

I hope you enjoyed the book! I would love to hear your feedback—I personally read every review. If you have three minutes to help me, can you please post a short review on the platform from which you purchased this book?

Also, I would be honored if you would sign up for my mailing list to keep updated on my upcoming books, exclusive content, special promotions, and events. Plus, as a subscriber, you'll have the opportunity to **download my new books for free** in exchange for an honest review. Your feedback is important to me and will help me improve my books and reach a wider audience. Scan to QR code to sign up.

Best, Michael Barton

Milton Keynes UK
Ingram Content Group UK Ltd.
UKHW021150111224
3520UKWH00091B/61

9 781922 435514